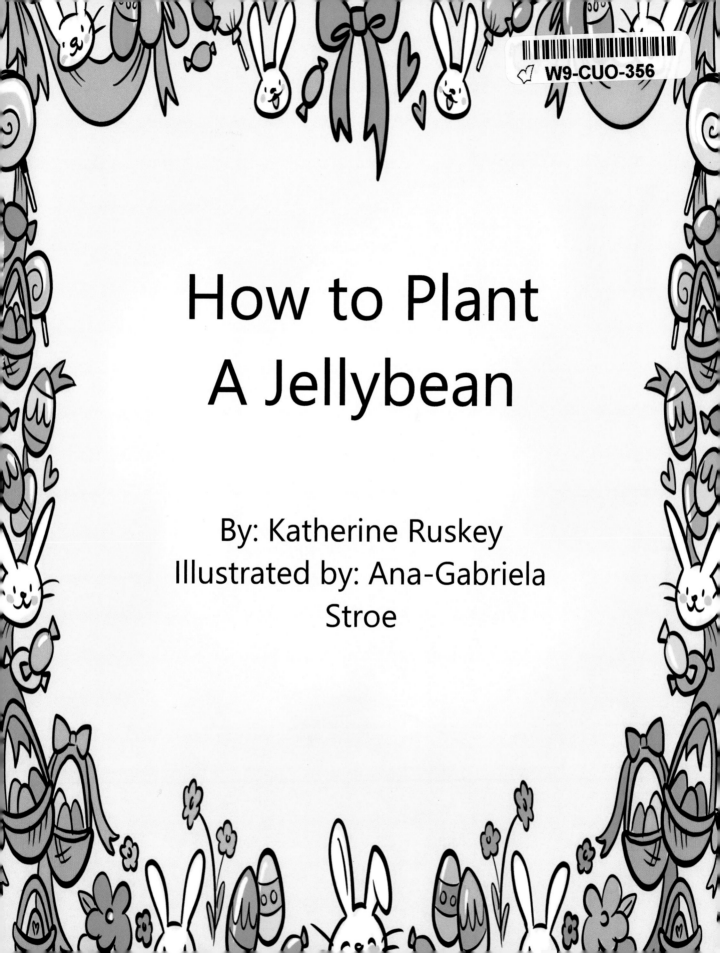

How to Plant A Jellybean

By: Katherine Ruskey
Illustrated by: Ana-Gabriela Stroe

For Maggie-
Because we really saw him

The night before
Easter

Excited for sweets

Waiting for the
Easter Bunny

To leave you some
treats

What better way
Than to make a
new tradition

Let's plant some
jellybeans

So carefully
listen!

Gather some jellybeans

The big and the small

All different flavors

You can plant them all!

Outside in the garden

Find the perfect spot

Plant in the ground

Or a flower pot

Place your
finger
Into the ground
Then carefully
drop
In little holes
around

No need to
water
Just cover
with a patter
Back in the
house
Into jammies
you scatter

Time for
the carrots
Grab a small
plate
Write a quick
note
Before it gets
too late

You fall asleep
that night

Dreaming of
sugar

While the Easter
Bunny comes
Ready to deliver

Skipping and
hopping

Wheel barrow full of
baskets

Wearing his purple
overalls

And a stunning green
jacket!

The jellybeans that
you planted

Are beginning to
sprout

His magic dust is sprinkled

And more start to pop out

The jellybeans grow

And more begin to bloom

Before you know it-

There's hardly any room!

The Easter Bunny brought magic

It's dancing in the air

The next morning you wake

Out the window you stare

All through the garden

Blooms of lollipops grew

From the jellybean planting

Easter magic and you!

About the Illustrator

Ana-Gabriela Stroe is a Romanian illustrator based in Denmark. She always loved to draw and can't remember wanting to be anything but an artist. After her studies in Graphic Design , she was drawn naturally toward the fascinating world of illustration. Since illustrating her first children's book in 2014, she went on to illustrate almost a dozen published books and also work on many other exciting projects, from board games to toy graphics.